Book 4: clip 3 music show by Wendy

Sunday 27th 2/05

[illegible]

★ Book tickets magic show 30$ by Thursday
Sunday 27th

E - Event
T - Together

MM	M	T	W	T	F	S	S
	2-10	x	x	3-11	3-11	5-1	2-10
Kf	4:30-12:30	9:00? 12:	9-5	9-5	4am	4am	x 7pm.

1345 225

Manufactured by Amazon.ca
Acheson, AB

14206007R00068